Justice Restored 2.0

A series of writings and poems from incarcerated youth

D1248163

Justice Restored 2.0

A series of writings and poems from incarcerated youth

Writings provided by Incarcerated Youth

Edited by Davon Clark

ISBN-13: 978-1-943610-11-2

ACKNOWLEDGMENTS

We would like to thank Camden County Juvenile Detention Center in NJ and Chester County Youth Center in PA for allowing us to conduct an Anthology book series workshop. Thank you to all the youth who participated. Without your participation this book could and would not exist. Thank you to Jan Michener of AHHAH for helping us conduct the workshops. Special thanks to Jayne Thompson and Christopher Murray for sharing their talents during several of the many workshops.

EDITOR'S NOTE

The juvenile youth centers request that we identify all contributors by either a first name, first name with last name initial, or by first and last name initials. Therefore, all the authors contributions are recognized by so.

DEDICATION

We dedicate this book to youth in the juvenile justice system whose voices have been marginalized. To all youth who feel lost, misguided or misunderstood. We believe through sharing your true pains, struggles and journeys; you help to break down the walls that defy and stereotype youth in the juvenile system. We thank you for your courage.

If interested in getting your detention/youth center, high school or organization involved with ADC Kid email us at iamadckid@gmail.com.

For more information regarding both Arts Holding Hands and Hearts and ADC Kid visit www.artsholdinghandsandhearts.com or www.adckid.com.

TABLE OF CONTENTS

Introduction

In July of 2015, Davon Clark was offered the opportunity to conduct a workshop at the Chester County Youth Center through AHHAH (Arts Holding Hands and Hearts). AHHAH is an expressive arts and literacy based program. Its mission is to empower youth, strengthen families, and mobilize the community through literacy, mindfulness and expressive arts. The organization was founded by Jan Michener with the hopes of bringing about a catharsis through the arts.

During the workshop Davon discussed his company ADC Kid (A Davon Clark Kid), children's books and more. (ADC Kid is a children's media company dedicated to the advancement of empowering and enlightening through literacy, fitness and basic math skills.) He brought along a young lady named Desarae Brown who is an aspiring comic book artist. She talked about her first comic book Dragon Thunder, Volume 1, what it takes to make a comic and her stint at the Art Institute. From there, the youth and staff explored the theme of superheroes in comics. They took a journey in creating superhero powers, superhero group names, acting out scenarios and developing their comic books.

After the program ended, Jan approached Davon with a brochure of writings from the youth in the center. She explained how once a week they engage in an expressive writing workshop. During the workshop the youth write about their life experiences. Davon read the writings intently taking in all the pains, fears, laughter, regrets and realities of their lives. He was left silent for about five minutes. Davon knew then that their voices demanded to be heard.

Through that, Davon sought out to develop an Anthology series book, which would include the voices of incarcerated youth. In August of 2015, Davon began joining Jan as she hosted numerous workshops at the Chester County Youth Center, Coatesville Area Public Library and Lincoln University, Coatesville Campus. The youth poured into the workshops not knowing what to expect. Every workshop Jan explored different forms of art to get the youth involved and talking. Such workshops consisted of music, dance and imagination, which eventually brought about the youth expressing themselves through writing.

While participating in the many workshops, Davon was conducting his own workshop at the Camden County Juvenile Detention Center. The workshop helped the youth set the ground work and develop their children's book. However, after a trial run Davon knew the particular subject of writing a children's book did not interest the youth. He left the detention center thinking what would spark an interest in the youth. That is when it clicked. Why not utilize their authentic voices and personal stories.

In November of 2015, Davon and Jan entered the Camden County Juvenile Detention Center with hopes of having the youth express themselves through a series of expressive writing workshops. When the youth came into the room they were full of disinterest, and tired after being woken up from a nap. Davon began by re introducing himself to the new youth and discussing what the workshop entailed. He was followed by Jan who in turn explained her involvement in the workshop. The youth sat there sucking their teeth and twisting their mouths up. It was immediately noticeable that they could care less for what the two were trying to bring to the center.

Jan took in a deep breath then dove into some yoga practices with the youth. The youth looked around the room taking each other in, unsure of what to make of it. After a minute or two of resistance a young man began to follow along. His actions invoked another young man to follow suit. From there, two more young men joined in. The room started to vibrate with the sound of breathing and humming from the yoga chants.

Some of the youth started to relax and let their guards down. However, there were still a few hesitant to reveal themselves in a room filled with their peers and new faces. Jan immediately rushed over to the uninterested youth full of energy and asked them to join in. The young men looked at each other and laughed slowly beginning to fall into the routine.

Once the warm up was completed, Jan and Davon began to instruct the youth through a series of ice breaker games; such as cross the line and say your name/something about yourself. These games allowed for the youth to become comfortable within their surroundings, and take notice of the similarities in which others around them possessed.

Jan followed the ice breaker games with a safe place/room agreement. This agreement acknowledged that everything said or acted out in the room would stay in the room. Nothing the youth talked about or did would leave the room. The purpose of this is to secure the youth's trust, knowing whatever they say/do would not be held/used against them.

These agreements lead Jan, Davon and the youth into a safe space to talk. The youth began to express themselves by sharing and engaging in creative writing through such forms as- short stories, poems, and more. Jan and Davon continued to lead the workshops throughout the months at both the Camden County Juvenile Detention Center and Chester County Youth Center. The youth continued to open up more and more each class. Jan continued to lead each class with a yoga warm up, and followed it with an activity before the writing process.

The last day of the program, Jayne Thompson the editor and creator of *"Letters to My Younger Self, An Anthology of Writings by Incarcerated Men at S.C.I. Graterford"* and Christopher Murray, one of the authors in the book co facilitated a workshop at both the Chester County Youth Center and Camden County Juvenile Detention Center. A lively discussion by Christopher, Jayne and the youth pursued. The youth asked many questions regarding the men who shared their stories/ lives in the book; such as, "What crime did they commit?", "How many years did they get?", "Do they have any children?", "Where are they from?" and more. Both guest did their best to answer certain questions without giving away to much information regarding said person's life and name. When Jayne and Christopher finished talking the youth were in awe.

These experiences, encounters and workshops led to the youth's writings shared in this book. We hope this book will bring greater understanding to the lives, fears, joys and pains of youth in the juvenile justice system.

A dilapidated row home sits in Camden, NJ with inspiring memorials and words on it to uplift the people in the community.

Prologue

Go the Distance

If I was you then..

I could've told you be one with yourself.

Stay true to your personality, in other terms know yourself.

Because the life you begin to live isn't the same as everyone else.

You are *DIFFERENT!*

You can alter your future if you go the distance.

Creating your own path amongst others existence.

There are many that will try to pull you down,

but you must show resistance.

Go the Distance.

- Shareef P.

LIFE

THE THINGS WE EXPERIENCE!

A homeless man on the streets of Camden, NJ trying to earn some money to eat.

What am I not saying?

It really makes me wonder.

Is there a secret message inside of me,

Inside of my mind,

Deep, deep down in my mind?

If so, is that the key to release me,

From this wretched struggle,

So that I can lead a wonderful life,

Or is the message better left alone?

Will it make me or break me?

Oh, how I wonder.

There's only one way to find out,

So I'll let my mind wonder!

- *E.W.*

I Have A Story To Tell

I lived with my mom when I was about 12. My dad got out of jail and moved in with us. I was confused because my mom always told me how much she hated my dad.

Eventually, after a month, things started going down hill. My dad got fired and started arguing with my mom a lot.

I suspected that he was using drugs again, and I was right. I was snooping through his drawers and found needles in there. I also caught him smoking crack in the bathroom.

The next day, I came home from school to find cops at my house. My dad had stolen 2 TVs, 2 laptops, a computer, and old cell phones and sold them for drugs. There was white residue on the coffee table and cops everywhere. They were asking my mom all kinds of questions.

The next day he was arrested at Walmart because he beat an old lady up and stole her purse.

I remember going to visit him a week later in jail, and that was the last time I saw him again for 4 years. Back to jail he went, and on with my life I went.

Just thinking about this made me tear up. I always wanted attention and love from my dad, but I never got it. I just always try to remind myself that he is sick. Addiction is a disease, and he is just sick.

- K. M. B

LIFE

I am a 17 year old boy. I go by Ky. All my life I have been trapped in the dark, not knowing what I was. My mother was trying to turn me into something I wasn't. I have been thrown the most, but never noticed like a ghost. It took time to find where I stand in life, but truth is like a coin I flip. My anger has taken control of my life, like the way you need a bullet to shoot a gun. But at the end of the day this is a game we play called LIFE.

- Ky-lee

The Monster

It's a game again.

Going away again.

All because I picked up the monster again.

All because I gave up, again.

All because I gave in.

I let love take control.

I let the ice fill my lungs.

I let the monster fill my veins.

I let it all go to keep myself sane.

Thought giving my all would make them stay.

All I wanted was to feel warm from the monster.

And love from the leader.

All I felt was chills from the monster.

Sickness from the monster.

Sweat from the monster.

Pain and defeat from the monster.

I felt love and fear from the leader.

I felt bruises and pain.

I felt control and again,

Defeat.

The monster destroyed my life again.

But the leader destroyed the girl I once was,

The feelings I once had.

The love I once had.

- *S.W.*

Addiction

I struggle everyday with this thing called addiction.

I don't think it will ever go away,

but that's just a prediction.

I stopped playing sports, and stopped going to school,

I just let myself go,

and I thought it was cool.

In came the drugs,

out went my life.

It's really hard to believe

I threw it all away over one night.

One time,

that's all it took.

I picked up that bag of dope.

Never in a million years did I think I would be hooked.

From pain killers, to cocaine, and heroin too.

It ruined my life,

and it will do the same to you.

Addiction is a disease,

there is no such cure.

I will be battling this my whole life,

but it will get easier,

I'm sure.

Nobody understands how serious this really is,

that it's killing thousands every day,

and many of them are only kids.

I want people to see what drugs did to my life,

I lost all my friends,

Because they knew it wasn't right.

Just remember,

one time is all it took,

 for me to throw my life away.

I pray to God and regret my decisions,

 every single day.

- K. M. B

I am The Chosen One

Home is a place,

where addiction takes place.

I see and hear,

what I'm suppose to do.

But I never follow thru.

My guidance struggled too.

Success is a taste,

that only follows

at my own pace.

When I think of home,

I think of hope,

because an addict never likes

to admit the feelings

of the word

Nope.

- C.G

ME

I am stubborn,

I didn't like the way I was raised.

I thought I could burn,

I didn't need to be praised.

I am rude

I am fazed

Many thought I was snude

I grew on struggle,

my life was a tuggle,

but now I see light

that makes me want to fight.

I am me!

Many can not see

the way I can be,

but you think how you can be new.

I used to cry,

but now I pray.

I am D.L.H

The person who used to be like….

YOU!

- D.L.H

I remember when I was a baby, my mom wanted to leave me in the hospital and my dad took me in. I remember watching 1:10 and Stitch, Strawberry Shortcake.

I remember when my mom and dad got back together and mom used to take me to Chuck E Cheese.

One day I caught my mom cheating on my dad. It was my dad's friend and I saw stuff I wasn't supposed to see and I got angry inside.

I wanted to tell my dad but I was afraid to. It hurt me so bad. I knew what was going on.

I remember my mom used to take me to the library.

I remember waking up at night to my mom and dad drunk and yelling at each other.

I remember when they were throwing things and my mom was yelling my name as she was running out of the house. I never saw her after that, until she started dating the guy she cheated on my dad with.

She tried stealing me and my dad wouldn't allow me to see her. So, I haven't seen her years after that.

As I got older she sent me letters and my older sister hid them from me. She didn't even like my mom. They never got along when we all lived together. When I turned 12 I saw letters in the mail and I went in the house and I found letters in my sister's room. I yelled at her and asked her why would you hide the letters and I was furious. She gave me all the letters she hid from me.

In one letter was my mom's number. So I gave her a call and she was asking me a lot of questions.

She came to see me one time and I remember I cleaned the whole house I was so excited and she asked my sister if she can take her and I to a bar. I thought she quit drinking and so they went to the bar.

They came home and my mom was wasted and she tried taking me with her but my sister didn't allow it.

I remember my dad was in jail and my sister finally agreed to let me spend one weekend with her and so I did.

She decided to try to keep me and one night my mom took me to the park. She invited friends who had beers and I was asleep in the park. I woke up with no shoes and I remember looking for my shoes and this man comes up to me and was drunk and he offered to help find my shoes. My mom introduced me to all her friends and took me to a guy's house. Mom left me there.

- S.E

Worth It

I see this place, I feel content.

I need to get this over with.

I see success, I feel regret.

I need to change.

I am worth it.

I see strength, I feel weakness.

I need help.

I want to succeed.

I am WORTH it.

I wonder why sometimes I hear my fear,

I see my accomplishments, I want my future.

I am worth it.

I pretend to fail, I feel no sorrow.

I touch my dreams.

I worry, but am in no hurry.

I cry to cover I am Worth it.

I understand myself, but am never understood.

I dream a future.

I hope to overcome.

I am worth it.

I am a survivor.

I am willing.

I am open minded.

I am an achiever.

I am worth it.

I'm worth a life of full fulfillment,

same as you.

- *C. G.*

LOVE

IS WHAT SHAPES US!

A shelter feeds the homeless people of Camden, NJ.

A Letter to My Unborn Child

Although I never got to meet you,

You had already stolen my heart,

From the day I found out about you,

 I never wanted us to be apart.

I looked forward to seeing your little smile and watching you grow.

Oh how your mother would have loved that too.

Whether you're here or with God, you're still my child.

When I glance at the sky I see your smile,

When I lay down at night I can feel your presence.

Even though I know you're flying high in heaven,

I know this is not goodbye for one day we'll meet,

 Then we can fly together.

That will be oh so great.

You may not walk on this earth,

But you walk in my heart.

I never wanted this to happen, it killed my mind,

But it's slowly reviving cause I know you're fine.

Me and your mother miss you.

We think about you every day.

But, honestly I just wanted to say how much I love you and how much I miss you,

And if I close my eyes I can feel your kisses.

Now we shall wait till the day we meet,

You can show me how to fly after we greet.

I love you, Fly high.

Your father.

- *E.W.*

Love

Love is in my eyes

Love is in my heart,

and now I can see why.

I wasn't even born when you died, but sometimes I still want to cry.

I know momma was hurting burying you

Uncle Mar was breaking down carrying you.

I wish you could really be here with us,

but somewhere we know there is an angel looking over us.

If I ever see you

I will give you a big hug and say

I LOVE YOU!

- DaQuaj T.

What Is Love?

What is love?

A genuine care

Something you feel, something you share.

A partner or two

One is me, one is you.

Somewhere down the line something was missing.

It was times you wasn't there to listen.

- *Tamiyah S.*

Hard Time

All my life it was hard and rough,

I'll be in the streets robbing homes and acting tough.

I had no one to love me until age 7,

then I was good until 11.

Then I was in trouble once again,

no one to turn to not even my friends.

I ran away from all my programs,

but kept the girl that found my romance.

- Joe

Grandma

Grandma growing up no matter what you always looked beautiful

No matter how bad we were, if we asked for it you would surprise us with our wishes- that was the best.

My love for you is eternally unconditional

Remember you brought me my bike?

Oh my god, I had to have fallen over a dozen times.

You always were there to catch me.

Telling me to " KEEP TRYING! DON'T GIVE UP! "

You made me the most driven person I am today.

I LOVE YOU GRANDMA

- Shareef P.

Love, Pain, Shame

My life is love, pain and shame

Who can I blame?

Nobody but myself

I was in control with my actions,

the love that was around for me I was blind by it,

even though they called me out of my name.

Who can I blame?

I don't care

they don't know me.

I am who I am

I will stay positive

realize the gift you have,

and don't be a shame.

Never give up!

- *Casche*

I Just Thought You Should Know

Dear Dad,

I just thought you should know what I'm doing now.

I am a smart, strong person who spends a lot of time trying to fix himself.

I just thought you should know how I'm feeling.

I am mad because of the fact you left.

I just thought you should know what I've been through.

Since the last time I saw you, I have lost so much. The time that I almost died when I was in the mix was especially important.

I just thought you should know what I wish for the future.

I hope that you can be here to protect me.

I just thought you should know what I miss a lot.

I miss the way we used to watch all the sport games that came on tv.

I just thought you should know I am glad you're back here with me.

- R.B

The Birth

I am the only one in the world that can tell you how I felt when my son was born.

I was crying and happy to meet him.

I told him "I love you! And I will be back soon."

I kissed him on his forehead and he smirked.

His eyes lighted up with joy.

This was a new life in front of me, that I created.

I knew now I could not let him down.

My mind could only think of his sounds.

I knew then I had to be around.

- *Unknown*

Where I Am From

I'm from a loving family.

I'm from a mom who always asked "Where are you going?" I would always say "No where, No where far." Be home before it gets to late.

I always lost track of time.

I am from Centerville.

I am from a street filled with dirt bikes, fast cars doing 100 down the street, police everywhere.

People smoking cigs,

Pushing strollers, kids coming home from school

I skipped and hopped when I was young.

It stopped when I found out females don't like guys who skipped and hopped.

I am from a family going to Third & 8th St. Baptist Church.

I'm from fried chicken and yellow rice and collard greens and corn bread.

I am from wanting my mom to know I love her. She has been with me through thick and thin. She's the real MVP.

- Oakley

STREETS

IS WHAT MAKES US!

A cop car patrolling the streets of Camden, NJ.

People Throwing Shade

People throwing shade

People tryna hide away

I'm just tryna make it to see another day

people keep pushing you till you break and snap

But when that 40 pops they don't know how to act

I always thought I'd be sweet and innocent

Look at me now into all types of different shit

these streets simply ain't for everybody

Messed around everything

including family

got taken from me.

- *Brittany G.*

I am from the world of gang members, killers, robbers and drug dealers.

Where the air is full of hatred, pain, suffering, and pride.

Where you hear sounds of crying, gunshots, arguing and sirens day and night.

Where people will shoot rather than fight.

Where loyalty is the key to the street.

Where people are being killed for a tweet.

Where kids look up to trapping on a block.

Where lives are saved by a glock.

Where people look for family in a gang.

Where people are being killed for a chain.

Where people are judged on their street name, rather than their story and pain.

Where people are called punks and lame, because they don't wanna play the thug game.

- Jacob

I am from Camden

I am from the hood where all you see is trash on the ground and the homeless on the side of the curb sleeping.

The smell of garbage trucks,

dogs fighting other dogs

I am from grand theft auto and 2 k 15, playing alone in my bedroom,

sitting in the bed playing the game on a 55" TV flat screen

My mom gave the TV to me

My mom is nice, kind and something evil

She'll throw a shoe at me while we're messing around

I'm from IHOP and Golden Corral

I'm from being told "I'm a dumpster baby. I'm not your real mother"

I'm from believing in God, but not in church

I'm from my uncle who was the greatest man who committed suicide when I was 14. I was there, I walked in and found him dead. I was scared. My dad took me to get pizza, I didn't tell him about my uncle

My uncle was found the next morning by his girlfriend. It makes me sad even today, I love him still.

- La Quan

Street Life

Always running these streets

never yell defeat

the streets was my life

now I can't seem to get my life right

Out day and night

tryna hustle light

on the side

you know how it is

it's do or die

- *Brittany G.*

I Come From..

I come from crack deals,

To living in abandoned houses,

To living on people's couches,

Selling pouches,

To get food and water.

Messing around with people's daughters.

Smoking the Ganja everyday,

To forget your feelings.

Getting into battles about people on your block doing Dealings.

Everyone stealing to get a buck,

People in the struggle stuck,

People on the block not giving a Fuck.

People gettin locked for life.

People using a pen as a knife.

I'm from the struggling streets.

I'm from sleeping on a blanket and one sheet.

Hearing a cold cell block door slam.

People never getting out of the jam,

People in life without a plan.

I'm from the trap,

That's not on the map.

- S.T.

Streets

When I was younger I thought life was a game,

but growing up things wasn't the same.

People switchin lanes,

I was runnin the streets like its funny,

til a gun got pointed to my head like a dummy,

only 17

yet living like I'm 20.

The streets ended up taking everything from me.

- *Breezy G.*

DEATH

IS WHAT CREATES US!

A stairway filled with blunt wrappers, personal possessions, piss, feces, needles and more inside Northgate Apartments located in North Camden, NJ.

Letter After a Time to My Late Brother

Here's something I never told you while you were alive....That I looked up to you. Always felt safe around you. Wanted to be just like you. You were like the father I never had.

Many times, since you've been gone, I've thought about...If you were still here. Giving up in life. Doing whatever it took to be with you again. Losing my life in the same way you lost yours.

Here's what's new in my life...I'm like you a little. Just more conservative with my actions and emotions. Im back with my mom. I have three sisters. I was stabbed and shot at. I been arrested. I still try not to let my anger get to me and make it in life like you told me before you died.

When I dream sometimes I imagine....Us back together. how life would be if you were still here. If I would have to be so hard in the streets if I had my big brother here still.

It's amazing to look ahead in my life and think....I might be able to do what we both had dreamed of doing together. Or the fact I try so hard in keeping my word I gave to you before you died in my arms.

- Jacob

Death

Death is something that can't be forgotten.

The past is the past, but what you go through in this life will not last.

I got friends that say they real, but I know that's a lie.

Late at night my mom use to worry about me; I told her don't cry don't cry, but when my brother died that's all she could do.

I think to myself life is always so dark, but I just gotta sit back and play my part.

I'm only 16 and seen a lot of shit growing up.

So when my brother died I felt like it was my fault.

What I'm trying to say is don't give up, just keep praying and put God first and family second.

- Brandon S.

In Life

Everyone will experience death, However not everyone lives

You are giving life with your 1st breath

And receive death with your last

In Life

Your judged based on character or class,

and your acts in the past

In Life

People will fall, cry and die

Personally, I choose to stay down and hide my feelings deep inside

In Life

You will need help, but pride will cause you to deny

In Life

Friends will come and go

Some fast, some slow

In Life

You are dealt a hand to play, R. I. P to the cards I lost

I wish they were back everyday

- Jacob S.

Tragic Situation

In my eyes I see a blue sky.

When people die their soul go to that blue sky.

With families left behind,

and a love one gone.

It's a tragic situation

Hearts broken

Wet cries mostly every night,

once the rain hits the ground

The heaven gates has opened.

Rest In Peace

- Casche

Letter to My Angel

Dear Mom,

You left that day without a glance;

not knowing god wasn't giving you a second chance.

So many thoughts left un read

So many words left un said

Wishing I could apologize for the stuff I did

All the lies, back talking, and bad things I did as a kid

Now you have your wings soaring through the sky.

I just sit and wonder why

God never gave me and you our last good bye.

I miss you so much it makes my heart ache.

But I stand strong not allowing my feelings to get to me, so I won't break.

Goodbyes are not forever

Goodbyes are not the end, they simply mean I'll miss you until we meet again.

- Justin G.

My Pain

My 5th birthday,

The sounds of gun shots.

Not knowing what had happened,

as blood hits the window and lands on my new clothing

like a splat of paint....

Screamin' from the top of my lungs

"Daddy, Daddy!"

but no answer.

I was 5 years old with no daddy,

but his permanently stained blood on my clothing to remind
me of him.

A year after my father's death on my 6th birthday,

my uncle got shot.

I asked myself why me?

What was I doing wrong?

It seemed every time my birthday came along,

another loved one was killed.

I was now 8 years old and still trying to get over both deaths

and my mom on the side,

not with me when I needed her the most.

Turning 9 was the day I never saw my mom again.

It was early in the morning and we had slept the night at my aunts.

My mom told me she'd be right back.

I am 16 years old now and still haven't heard from her....

- Imani

Epilogue

No More Pain In Those Tears

No More Pain In Those Tears

When I cry it seems like no one cares.

I was scared it was death in my eyes that's my only fear,

But the law don't understand to care.

The prosecutor didn't know it was kill or be killed

all they see is my history in the past with the law.

30 years because of my fear?

I thought to myself they just trying to get in my ear

I could see my mother's tears

she knew her baby's life was over in the courtroom,

she also knows it's a better place than the streets or death.

My death was her fear,

I'm sorry mom.

I couldn't let that happen.

No More Pain In Those Tears

Every night when I cry I know I will make it,

just take it slow get my mind right.

56

Some people throw dirt on my name

some people dust it off because they care.

They know I am one of a kind....

One day I will have my freedom and the sun will shine

I pray better days to come.

I will keep my head up high and wipe those tears.

Grab a hand and pray,

Father God forgive me for my sins I have done in the past give me the strength to heal from that

Take the demons away and fear no evil within me.

In your name I pray AMEN.

- *Casche*

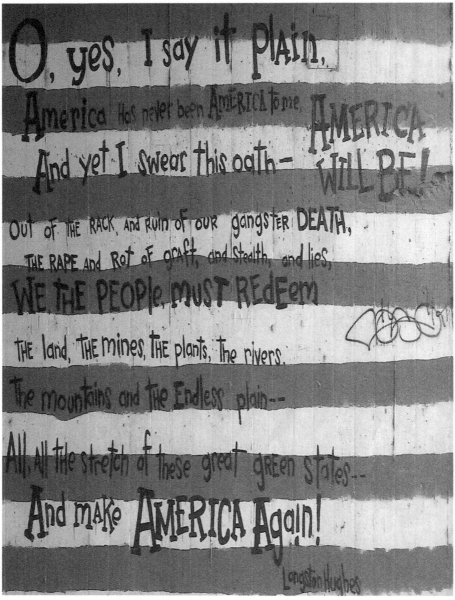

Langston Hughes memorials sit under a bridge in Centerville, Camden, NJ.

Discussion

Now we challenge you to have an open ended discussion around the themes in the book.

Prompt Questions

1. Was there a certain story or poem in which you connected to? Why? _____

   _____

   _____

   _____

   _____

2. Which theme of writings stuck out the most to you? Why? _____

   _____

   _____

   _____

   _____

BONUS
WRITINGS

Running

I am always running.

It started with running towards school.

Then I was running from the bullies.

Then I was running towards a fight.

When I turned 14, I started running towards friends.

I was running from cops and bullets and even ops.

I was running from my thoughts everyday I opened my eyes.

I used to be always sad and depressed.

I started using drugs.

I popped perks with my dealers,

Even drank and smoked weed.

When I was upset my happy place was the weed and codeine.

I was running from my feelings, holding them inside.

Trying to make sure I didn't show my sadness,

I hid it with a smile.

Now I'm here.

When I go home,

I'm going to run towards my dreams.

My future is bright.

I do not belong here surrounded with four walls and a metal door.

I'm going to run to my freedom.

- *Starr*

I Feel, I See

Angry.

I feel like the tide of the ocean

Going IN and OUT.

Depressed, Upset, Lost, Unfocused, Forgotten,

Motivated, Successful.

I feel like a shadow.

Everyone looks at my negative past

Instead of giving a me chance

To prove myself and be positive

Out in the community.

They only see the drugs and mistakes I have made.

I see you.

But you don't see me doing right, being a successful young man.

I see hatred and disappointment from the Judge.

I am constantly being judged by words on a piece of paper.

Everyday I give respect to gain respect in return.

People doubt me;

But it motivates me to work harder towards success.

I will chase my dreams, and make them come true

No matter what anyone thinks of me.

My arms will reach out to others.

I see a bright future for myself in the long run.

- *Tyler*

I Am A Warrior

I am a wonderful and peaceful person.

I wonder when I get mad where my mind takes me.

I hear voices sometimes when I get angry.

I see things so clearly now since I've been in so many places.

I want to be successful in the "law" part of my life.

I am grateful for my happiness.

I pretend that I am okay when I'm really not.

I feel out of place when I am with younger people.

I touch certain peoples' lives.

I worry about my future wife and kids.

I cry when I lose people that I am close to.

I am misunderstood a lot.

I understand my anger is out of control sometimes.

I feel safe in detention.

I am grateful for my time here;

Honestly, I would have never graduated high school,

I would have probably died a couple years ago,

I wouldn't have so much going for me right now,

Because now I have a clean sheet,

I'm less addicted to marijuana,

And I am more focused than ever on my future.

I dream that one day I will be at peace,

Filled with love and kindness in my soul.

I am a warrior!

- Stefon

When I was REALLY LITTLE, I ran away from nightmares.

I was afraid of being alone.

At the time, I ran toward being an author, model and gas station owner.

I dreamed about being successful on my own in multiple aspects.

When I got a LITTLE OLDER, I ran away from myself.

When I ran, I expected that everyone would leave me alone, finally.

At the time, I ran toward losing myself, and drugs.

When I ran, I hoped for peace of mind from myself.

TODAY when I run, I run away from suffocating anxiety

and depression that drowns me.

More than anything I wish I could run from medication and therapy,

Hiding Me.

TODAY when I run, I run toward college.

More than anything I wish I could run to 10 years from now.

- Gabby

I See You, You Don't See Me

I see you, you don't see me.

It's like I'm looking through a two-way mirror at what life could be.

I'm in a place all alone and you have everybody,

Your friends and family,

While it's just me meeting strangers on the street.

Meanwhile I'm stuck in a cell.

YOU SEE paintings in a museum.

I SEE Art of the ones gone;

Who've once come but then left me.

Left me in a despair of dark.

I don't see what you quite see.

You hear laughter on the street.

I hear nothing.

Quiet is my enemy.

So you see, You don't see what I see, but I see you, and your all I wanna be

FREE!

- Nadiya

Where I'm From

I am from a place where most people wouldn't be proud to call home.

I am from a place where the only way to survive is to be a well-respected drug dealer or a killer.

At times it was kill or be killed.

I am from a place where you're supposed to be proud to say to people that it's your first day out, or that you were booked.

I am from a place where 24/7 you're watching your back.

A place where you're running from the cops or bullets.

A place where a nine year old can have easy access to a gun.

A place where you can't be afraid to fight.

A place where your friend is killed in front of your school.

I am from a place where,

You weren't cool if you didn't smoke, or did codeine, or popped perks.

I am from a place where you always see RIP put in front of someone's house or T-shirt.

Even though I am from here on the outside,

I am not any of these things.

I've put RIP in front of many people's names, and

I have ran from bullets.

I am from Chester, Pennsylvania,

But Chester doesn't make me

Who I AM!

- Starr

4 Walls and a Metal Door

I remember when I was 13 going on 14

It was my first birthday without my family, in Juvie.

Somehow, I knew it wouldn't be my last without them, I guessed.

I was right, because the next year

On my 15th birthday,

All I saw was 4 walls and a metal door.

Years pass by and my life just keeps repeating itself.

Finally, I'm 17, still locked up,

I make a promise that this year, 2017,

I will be free on my birthday

And my life will change,

I will get out of the SYSTEM.

I'm free.

Having the time of my life,

Catching up on my childhood, I missed.

Then 3 days before my birthday I almost loose it

"My Freedom."

July 31, 2017

I'm sitting in a squad car going to the situation.

August 1, 2017, I wake up,

There it is again.

4 Walls and a Metal Door.

I'm thinking to myself,

What Happened?

What did I do?

I fucked up.

I took advantage.

Here I am again in the same predicament the past 4 years.

I finally realized,

I am a Screw Up.

I'm Worthless.

I'm not going to do anything with my life.

I usually know what to say in court.

July 31st "My court date"

Judge asked, "What happened?"

"Why do you keep on messing up?"

For the first time

I don't have any excuses.

I say,

"I don't know."

I finally realize I can't blame anybody for what I did.

I fucked up.

I made the wrong decision.

I screwed my life up.

I gotta take the consequences.

I realize for the first time,

I'm not angry at other people because I just got booked.

NO!

I'm angry at myself.

I realize

I fuck up every opportunity I get.

I don't know what to do any more with myself

"What are they gonna do with me."

I ask myself.

They've done everything.

What's left?

I sit here and ask myself that same question

Over

And

Over

Again

Then everything goes blank.

I'm just sitting here looking at my cell door wondering

"What Now!"

- Dylan

Dear Big Brother

It's crazy how you left me out here in these streets alone;

Like why didn't you fight back that day when you was on the ground shot.

Knowing that you had a little brother at home that looked up to you.

Bro, I miss and I love you so much.

Like you watched me grow up to be a man.

Sometimes I ask God why couldn't he help you fight.

Why did he have to take you away from me.

Bro, ever since you died I shut down.

I fell to the streets, gang banging and selling drugs

Leading me to jail for a year, then I came home

Did the same shit, now I regret it.

Because I'm back in jail

Probably ready to do 3 to 5, for some bullshit.

But it's ard big brother, cuz I will be home soon

And doing good for you bro.

I love you

I know you are in heaven looking down and watching over me.

- Damion

Made in the USA
Middletown, DE
29 December 2018